Progress Tests

English

Louis Fidge

Age 8–9
Year 4
Key Stage 2

Hachette UK's policy is to use papers that are natural, renewable and recyclable products and made from wood grown in sustainable forests. The logging and manufacturing processes are expected to conform to the environmental regulations of the country of origin.

Orders: please contact Bookpoint Ltd, 130 Milton Park, Abingdon, Oxon OX14 4SB. Telephone: (44) 01235 827720. Fax: (44) 01235 400454. Lines are open 9.00a.m.–5.00p.m., Monday to Saturday, with a 24-hour message answering service. Visit our website at www.hoddereducation.co.uk.

© Louis Fidge 2013
First published in 2013 exclusively for WHSmith by
Hodder Education
An Hachette UK Company
338 Euston Road
London NW1 3BH

Impression number   10 9 8 7 6 5 4 3 2
Year   2018 2017 2016 2015 2014

This edition has been updated, 2014, to reflect National Curriculum changes.

Cover illustration by Oxford Designers and Illustrators Ltd
Illustrations by Fakenham Prepress Solutions, Fakenham, Norfolk NR21 8NN
Typeset in 16pt Folio by Fakenham Prepress Solutions, Fakenham, Norfolk NR21 8NN
Printed in Great Britain by Hobbs the Printers Ltd, Totton, Hampshire SO40 3WX

A catalogue record for this title is available from the British Library.

ISBN: 978 1444 188 882

Introduction

How this book can help your child

Each *English Progress Test* book is designed for your child to complete on their own, but you may like to work with them for the first few tests to give them confidence and to be sure they can do the activities independently. This is particularly important for the first two books in the series (for ages 5–6, and 6–7). If children need extra support do provide it, perhaps by reading the reading passage together with them.

How to use this book

To get the most from this book:

- Try to choose a quiet place for doing the tests. Try to avoid other distractions (like having the TV on at the same time!).
- Don't let children struggle over words they don't know. Let them have a good go first of all, but if they simply cannot work out the word, tell them what it is.
- Don't get your child to do too much at once. A 'little and often' approach is a good way to start.
- Your child should work systematically through the book, test by test.
- Do reward your child with lots of praise and encouragement. Be positive. Don't just comment on mistakes.
- Talk to your child about what they have learnt and what they can do.
- When they have read the reading passage, get them to check their understanding by working through the questions on the page opposite.
- The first section (**Checking understanding**) is made up of comprehension questions. The answers to these are always to be found in the text. (Some questions may need a bit more thinking about than others!)
- The second section (**Sentences**) checks children's understanding of sentence structure (grammar and punctuation etc.) linked to the passage.
- The third section (**Words**) checks children's understanding of spelling and vocabulary linked to the passage.
- Involve your child in marking the tests and talk together about any incorrect answers. Be sensitive and draw more attention to those that were correct, asking your child to tell you how they tackled the question and what they found difficult about it.
- When the marks for the test are added up, the results may be recorded on the record sheet (on the inside back cover). This will give you and the children, a sense of how well they are doing.

Long ago, a beautiful Greek princess, called Helen, was captured by soldiers from Troy, called Trojans.
Helen's husband, Menelaus, was so angry he sailed to Troy with an army to rescue her.

The Greek army fought many battles with the Trojans, but they could not get Helen back.
Then Menelaus had an idea. He ordered his men to make a huge wooden horse. Menelaus and his men climbed inside it through a secret door, and hid in it.

The next day, the Trojans saw the wooden horse and thought all the Greeks had gone home. They dragged the horse through the gates and into their city. Then they had a party.

That night, when the Trojans were asleep, the Greeks opened the secret door and crept out of the wooden horse.
They attacked the sleeping Trojans and beat them easily. Menelaus rescued Helen and took her back to Greece.

A Greek myth

Checking understanding

Answer these questions.

1. Who was captured by Trojan soldiers?   *Helen*
2. What was the name of Helen's husband?   *Menelaus*
3. Why did Menelaus take an army to Troy?   _____
4. Did the Greeks fight a lot of battles with the Trojans?   _____
5. What did Menelaus order his men to build?   _____
6. Where did Menelaus and his men hide?   _____
7. Where did the Trojans drag the wooden horse?   _____
8. Where did the Trojans think the Greeks had gone?   _____
9. When did the Greeks creep out of the horse?   _____
10. Why do you think the Greeks beat the Trojans so easily?   _____

Sentences

Write each sentence again, and punctuate it correctly.

11. long ago there was a beautiful greek princess called helen

_____

12. menelaus sailed to troy to rescue helen

_____

Words

Find a word in the story that rhymes with:

13. caught: _____   14. would: _____   15. floor: _____

Mark your answers. How well did you do?

I scored ____ out of 15.

One morning the North Wind and the Sun saw a horseman wearing a new cloak.

'That man looks pleased with his new cloak,' said the North Wind. 'I bet I could easily make him take it off if I wanted to.'

'I don't think you could,' the Sun replied. 'But let us both try to get him to take his cloak off. You go first.'

The North Wind began to blow, and blow, and blow. He blew so hard that people had to hold on to their hats. Leaves were blown off the trees and some ships in the harbour were sunk. He blew so hard all the animals were terrified. The North Wind blew with all his might, but it was no use. As he blew harder, the horseman just pulled his cloak more tightly around himself to keep warm.

Next it was the Sun's turn. He began gently to give out his heat. As he did so the insects hummed and flowers began to open. Birds began to sing. People became drowsy and lay down to sleep. The horseman began to feel very hot. When he came to a river, he took off his cloak and got off his horse for a rest under a shady tree.

Checking understanding

Write T (true) or F (false) after each sentence.

1. The North Wind and the Sun had a competition. _____
2. The horseman looked unhappy with his new cloak. _____
3. The North Wind and the Sun both tried to get the man to take his cloak off. _____
4. The Sun tried first. _____
5. The North Wind blew so hard that people had to hold on to their hats. _____
6. As the Wind blew, the man took off his cloak. _____
7. When the Sun shone, the birds began to sing. _____
8. When the Sun shone, people began to wake up. _____
9. When the Sun shone, the horseman began to feel hot. _____
10. The Sun won the competition. _____

Sentences

Complete each sentence with a sensible adjective.

11. The horseman was wearing a _____ cloak.
12. When the Sun shone, people became _____.
13. The horseman rested under a _____ tree.

Words

14. Change the 'h' in 'hummed' to 'dr' to make a loud noise: _____

15. Change the 'r' in 'river' to 'sh' to make a word meaning what you do when you are cold: _____

Mark your answers. How well did you do?

I scored _____ out of 15.

Rabbits

Rabbits live in tunnels underground called burrows. They come out at dawn and dusk to find plants to eat.

Badgers

Badgers live underground in a sett. They stay in their sett until night-time. Then they go out at night and look for food like frogs and mice.

Foxes

Foxes live in homes called dens. A den is usually a hole in a grassy bank. Foxes hunt for small animals like birds or mice at night.

Squirrels

Squirrels make their homes from twigs and leaves. A squirrel's home is called a drey. Squirrels come out in the daytime. They eat nuts, birds' eggs and sometimes baby birds.

Checking understanding

Choose the best word to fill in each gap.

1. Rabbits live in _____ (furrows, burrows).
2. Rabbits come out at dawn and _____ (dusk, tusk).
3. Rabbits eat _____ (ants, plants).
4. Badgers live in _____ (sets, setts).
5. Badgers come out at _____ (dawn, night).
6. Badgers eat frogs and _____ (rice, mice).
7. Foxes live in _____ (tens, dens).
8. Foxes eat small _____ (animals, boxes).
9. A squirrel's home is called a _____ (drey, grey).
10. Squirrels eat _____ (huts, nuts).

Sentences

Complete each sentence with a sensible verb.

11. Rabbits _____ in burrows.
12. Badgers _____ for food like frogs and mice.
13. Squirrels sometimes _____ baby birds.

Words

Do these word sums and make two compound words.

14. under + ground = _____
15. some + times = _____

Mark your answers. How well did you do?

I scored ____ out of 15.

The sea goes on forever

Verse 1   The rain drizzles and the rain falls
But the sea goes on forever.

Verse 2   Some plants bloom, then fade away
But the sea goes on forever.

Verse 3   The sun replaces the moon and stars
But the sea goes on forever.

Verse 4   Streams trickle and flow into rivers
But the sea goes on forever.

Verse 5   Leaves go green then turn yellow and brown
But the sea goes on forever.

Verse 6   Sundays soon become Mondays
But the sea goes on forever.

Verse 7   Spring – Summer – Autumn – Winter
But the sea goes on forever.

Verse 8   We grow older day by day
But the sea goes on forever.

Checking understanding

Answer these questions.

1. How many verses are there in the poem? _____
2. Are the words of the second line of each verse always the same? _____
3. Is Verse 1 about snow or rain? _____
4. Which word in Verse 2 means to produce flowers? _____
5. In Verse 3 what replaces the moon and stars? _____
6. In Verse 4 what do streams flow into? _____
7. What is the poem called? _____
8. Which verse mentions leaves? _____
9. Which verse mentions the four seasons? _____
10. What do we do in Verse 8? _____

Sentences

Complete each sentence with two sensible verbs.

11. In the poem, the plants _____ then _____ away.
12. In the poem, the rain _____ and the rain _____.

Words

Match one of these words to each description: rain   moon   river

13. the planet that circles the Earth and shines at night: _____
14. a large stream: _____
15. drops of water that fall from the sky: _____

Mark your answers. How well did you do?

I scored ____ out of 15.

Three butterflies were enjoying the sunshine. One was orange, one was yellow and one was white. Suddenly a big, black cloud appeared in the sky. It began to rain. 'Let's look for somewhere to shelter,' one butterfly said.

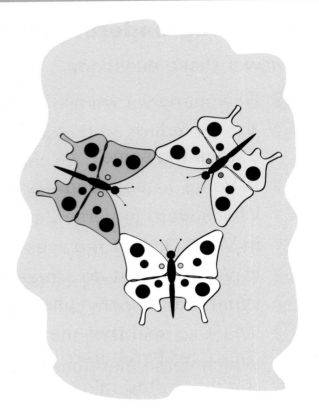

Nearby was a bed of lovely yellow roses. 'May we stop here until the rain passes?' the yellow butterfly asked one of the roses.
'You may,' replied the rose. 'You are the same colour as I am. The others will have to look elsewhere.'
'Well, I'm not staying without my friends,' the yellow butterfly said, and the three butterflies flew off.

Next they saw a tall white lily. 'May we stop here until the rain passes?' the white butterfly asked the lily.
'You may,' replied the lily. 'You are the same colour as I am. The others will have to look elsewhere.'
'Well, I'm not staying without my friends,' the white butterfly said, and the three butterflies flew off.

Last of all they came to an orange tulip. 'May we stop here until the rain passes?' the orange butterfly asked the tulip.
'You may,' replied the tulip. 'You are the same colour as I am. The others will have to look elsewhere.'
'Well, I'm not staying without my friends,' the orange butterfly said, and the three butterflies flew off.

Soon the rain cloud passed over and the sun came out again. The warmth of the sun dried the butterflies' wings. The sun seemed to smile down on them and say, 'Well done, little butterflies! You did the right thing. In life, you will always meet some people who are unkind and thoughtless. It's best just to ignore them and pass on.'

Checking understanding

Write T (true) or F (false) after each sentence.

1 Each butterfly was a different colour. _____

2 The butterflies went to look for shade because it was so hot. _____

3 The first flowers they came to were pink roses. _____

4 The yellow rose said the yellow butterfly could stop on it. _____

5 The yellow butterfly refused to stop without its friends. _____

6 The next flower they came to was the orange tulip. _____

7 The white butterfly asked the lily if they could all stop there until the rain passed. _____

8 The tulip said that the orange butterfly could stop, but the other two butterflies could not. _____

9 It did not stop raining all day. _____

10 The sun said that you will always meet some people who are unkind and thoughtless. _____

Sentences

Put in the missing speech marks in these sentences.

11 The yellow butterfly asked the yellow rose, May we stop here?

12 You may, replied the rose. You are the same colour as I am.

Words

Complete each word with the prefix 'un' or 'dis' to give it the opposite meaning.

13 _____kind   14 _____appear   15 _____well

Mark your answers. How well did you do?

I scored _____ out of 15.

Test 6: The mouse, the frog and the little red hen

Once a mouse, a frog and a little red hen
Lived together in a house.
The frog was a very lazy frog,
But lazier still was the mouse.

One day, Little Red Hen was out looking for food,
And she found a bag of rye;
Said she, 'Now who will make some bread?'
Said the lazy mouse, 'Not I.'

'Nor I,' croaked Frog as he dozed in the shade.
Red Hen made no reply,
But flew round with a bowl and a spoon,
And mixed and stirred the rye.

'Who will make the fire to bake the bread?'
Said the mouse again, 'Not I.'
The frog opened one sleepy eye,
And gave the same reply.

The little red hen never said a word.
A roaring fire she made;
And while the bread was baking brown,
'Who will set the table?' she said.

'Not I,' said the sleepy frog with a yawn;
'Nor I,' said the mouse again.
So the table she set, and put the bread on it,
'Who will eat this bread?' she said.

'I will!' cried the frog. 'And I!' squeaked the mouse
As they near the table drew;
'Oh no, you won't!' said the little red hen,
And away with the bread she flew.

Checking understanding

Answer these questions.

1. Which three animals lived together? _____
2. Who did all the work? _____
3. Which two animals were lazy? _____
4. What did Little Red Hen make the bread with? _____
5. What did she mix and stir the rye with? _____
6. What did they need to do to bake the bread? _____
7. When Little Red Hen asked Frog and Mouse to help set the table, what did they both reply? _____
8. When Little Red Hen asked Frog and Mouse who wanted to eat the bread, what did they both reply? _____
9. Did Little Red Hen let Frog and Mouse have any bread? _____
10. What did Little Red Hen do with the bread? _____

Sentences

Complete each sentence with a sensible adjective.

11. Frog did not help because he was very _____.
12. Little Red Hen made a _____ fire.
13. When he was asked to help set the table, the _____ frog said, 'Not I,' with a yawn.

Words

Complete these words correctly.

14. cr__ __k (the noise frogs make)
15. r__ __r (the noise lions make)

Mark your answers. How well did you do?

I scored _____ out of 15.

The only thing Bob could think of was water. He was very, very hot. The road was long and dusty. Then he saw a well. 'I expect it will be dry, like the last one,' he said to himself.

As he got closer, he saw a dog lying beside it. The dog was so thin that Bob could see its bones. 'I don't care about you,' he said to the dog. 'I just need water. Get out of my way.' The dog looked at him pitifully.

Bob was desperate to find some water. He picked up a stone and dropped it into the well. For a second there was silence and then PLOP. 'Water!' cried Bob excitedly.

There was no rope or bucket so Bob had to climb down the inside of the well. At last he reached the bottom. He poured some cool water over his head and drank great gulps of water until he felt completely satisfied.

Suddenly a picture of the skinny old dog came into his mind. 'He is just as much in need of a drink as I was,' Bob thought. 'But how can I get water up to him?' Just then a thought came into his head.

When he reached the top of the well the dog looked up. Bob smiled. 'Here you are,' he said and held out one of his boots – full to the brim with water!

Checking understanding

Choose the best word to fill in each gap.

Bob was very **1**_____ (hot, cold) and thirsty. When he came to a **2**_____ (road, well) there was a **3**_____ (thin, thick) dog next to it. Bob dropped a **4**_____ (rock, stone) into the well to see if there was any **5**_____ (food, water) at the bottom. There was no **6**_____ (hope, rope) or bucket, so Bob climbed down the **7**_____ (inside, outside) of the well. At the bottom he **8**_____ (splashed, poured) some cool water over his head. **9**_____ (Alfie, Bob) took some water up for the dog in his **10**_____ (boot, hat).

Sentences

Write each sentence again, and punctuate it correctly.

11 bob was very very hot _____

_____

12 as bob got closer he saw a dog near the well _____

_____

13 water cried bob excitedly _____

_____

Words

14 Find a word that ends with 'ate'. _____

15 Find a word that ends with 'ure'. _____

Mark your answers. How well did you do?

I scored ____ out of 15.

 A is for Alice who loves drinking and eating.

 B is for Ben who can't stop cheating.

 C is for Carol who tries to catch flies.

 D is for Danny who tells lots of lies.

 E is for Edward who is always late.

 F is for Florence who loves licking her plate.

 G is for Georgia who shouts and screams.

 H is for Harry who likes buying ice creams.

 I is for Ivan who pulls girls' hair.

 J is for Jade who will never share.

 K is for Kevin who won't wash his face.

 L is for Louise who enjoys a good chase.

 M is for Mark who gobbles his food.

 N is for Nicole who is ever so rude.

Checking understanding

Answer these questions. Who:

1 gobbles his food? _____

2 pulls girls' hair? _____

3 won't wash his face? _____

4 loves eating and drinking? _____

5 loves licking her plate? _____

6 will never share? _____

7 tries to catch flies? _____

8 can't stop cheating? _____

9 is always late? _____

10 shouts and screams? _____

Sentences

Write the next two lines of the poem again, and punctuate them correctly.

11 o is for olivia who breaks all her toys

_____

12 p is for petra who plays with the boys

_____

Words

Write each set of verbs in alphabetical order.

13 drinking   eating   cheating   _____ _____ _____

14 pulling   washing   licking   _____ _____ _____

15 shutting   sharing   shouting   _____ _____ _____

Mark your answers. How well did you do?

I scored ____ out of 15.

A loaf is made from wheat. A farmer grows the wheat. It needs plenty of rain and sunshine to grow.

A combine harvester cuts the wheat. The grains are put in a lorry and sent to a mill.

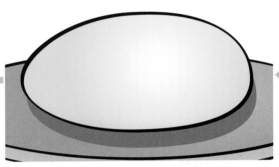

In a bakery, flour, fat, salt, water and yeast are mixed together into a dough. (The yeast makes the dough rise.)

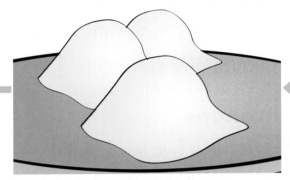

At the mill, the wheat grains are ground into flour.

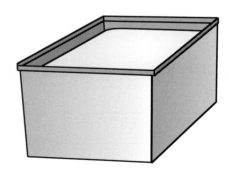

The dough is put into loaf-shaped tins and cooked in an oven.

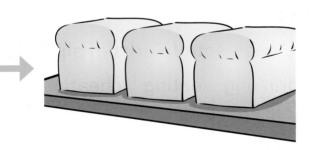

When they are cooked, the loaves are delivered to the shops for us to buy.

Checking understanding

Write T (true) or F (false) after each sentence.

1. A loaf is made from wheat. _____
2. Wheat needs plenty of rain and sunshine to grow. _____
3. A tractor cuts the wheat. _____
4. The wheat grains are sent to a pill. _____
5. At the mill, the wheat grains are ground into flour. _____
6. At the mill, flour, fat, salt, water and yeast are mixed together into a dough. _____
7. Yeast makes the dough rise. _____
8. The dough is put into oval-shaped tins. _____
9. The dough is cooked in an oven. _____
10. A bakery is where bread is cooked. _____

Sentences

Complete each sentence with a sensible verb.

11. A farmer _____ the wheat.
12. A baker _____ the bread.
13. We _____ the bread from a shop.

Words

14. Change the 'd' in 'dough' to 'c': _____ (we do this when we have a cold)
15. Change the 'o' in 'loaf' to 'e': _____ (something we see on a tree)

Mark your answers. How well did you do?

I scored ____ out of 15.

Alice was in a long hall, lit by lamps in the ceiling. There were doors all the way round, but they were locked. How was she going to get out?

Then she saw a little table made of glass. On top of it was a gold key. But it was too small to unlock any of the doors. Then Alice noticed a low curtain. Behind it she found a tiny door, only forty centimetres high.

Alice had to kneel down to look through the door. There was a small passage, not much larger than a rat hole, that led to the loveliest garden she had ever seen. But she was too big to get her head through the doorway.

'I wish I could close up like a telescope!' she said to herself.

She walked back to the glass table. To her surprise there was a bottle on it which she had not seen before. A label round its neck said DRINK ME in large writing. Alice took a sip. It was delicious and tasted of all of Alice's favourite foods. So she drank it up.

'What a curious feeling!' said Alice. 'I must be closing up like a telescope!' And so she was! Soon she was only twenty centimetres high, just the right size to go through the little door into the lovely garden.

Adapted from Alice's Adventures in Wonderland *by Lewis Carroll*

Checking understanding

Answer these questions.

1. How was the long hall lit? _____
2. What did Alice see on a little glass table? _____
3. How high was the door Alice found behind the curtain? _____
4. Why did Alice kneel down? _____
5. What did Alice see at the end of the small passage? _____
6. What did Alice wish she could close up like? _____
7. What surprised Alice when she walked back to the glass table? _____
8. What did the drink in the bottle taste like? _____
9. How small did Alice become? _____
10. Who wrote the book *Alice's Adventures in Wonderland*? _____

Sentences

Complete each sentence with a sensible preposition.

11. Alice saw a gold key _____ the glass table.
12. There was a tiny door _____ a low curtain.
13. Alice was too big to get her head _____ the doorway.

Words

Fill in the missing 'silent' letter at the beginning of each word.

14. __neel

15. __riting

Mark your answers. How well did you do?

I scored _____ out of 15.

23

This poem is a traditional song of the Teleut people of Siberia.

Siberia is a very flat, open country, where the wind is very powerful.

Trees with weak roots
I will strike, I the wind.
I will roar, I will whistle.

Houses not tightly roofed
I will destroy, I the wind.
I will roar, I will whistle.

Corn in the field
I will destroy, I the wind.
I will roar, I will whistle.

Haycocks built today
I will scatter, I the wind.
I will roar, I will whistle.

The worthless slug-a-bed
I will wake, I the wind.
I will roar, I will whistle.

Fire in the hearth
I will blow, I the wind.
I will roar, I will whistle.

Checking understanding

Complete each sentence correctly.

1. The poem is a traditional song of the Teleut people of S__b__r__ __.
2. Siberia is a very fl__t, open c__ __ntry.
3. The wind in Siberia is very power__ __ __.
4. The wind will str__ __ __ trees with weak r__ __ts.
5. The wind will sca__ __ er haycocks built today.
6. The wind will destr__ __ houses not t__ __ __ __ly roofed.
7. The wind will w__k__ the worth__ __ __ __ slug-a-bed.
8. The wind will destroy the c__ __n in the f__ __ld.
9. The wind will bl__ __ the fire in the h__ __rth.
10. The last line of each verse is always the s__m__.

Sentences

Complete each sentence with a sensible adjective.

11. The poem is a _____ song from Siberia.
12. Siberia is a very _____, open country.

Words

Complete each noun with the suffix 'ful' to make it into an adjective.

13. power__ __ __
14. wonder__ __ __
15. care__ __ __

Mark your answers. How well did you do?

I scored ____ out of 15.

Narrator: One day, Jasmine saw smoke and heard a voice calling to her from a cave. Out of the cave a big green dragon appeared. It looked friendly and was smiling.

Dragon: Don't worry. I won't eat you.

Jasmine: Well, that's a relief! I thought all dragons ate humans.

Dragon: I don't eat people nowadays. I've given that up.

Jasmine: What do you eat, then?

Dragon: I eat anything made of metal – cars, tractors, fences.

Jasmine: Are they good for you?

Narrator: The dragon laughed and swished his long tail and flapped his wings.

Dragon: Metal makes my wings and tail very strong.

Jasmine: Can you fly?

Dragon: Of course I can. Hop on my back and I'll show you.

Narrator: Jasmine hopped onto the dragon's back and put her arms around his neck. She made a face as she did so.

Jasmine: Ouch! Your scales are very prickly.

Dragon: Be careful you don't get too near my mouth.

Jasmine: Don't worry. I don't want to be burnt.

Dragon: Hold on tight. Off we go.

Narrator: The dragon flapped his wings and together they whooshed off up into the sky.

Checking understanding

Choose the best word to fill in each gap.

Jasmine saw **1**_____ (bats, smoke) coming from a
2_____ (cave, wave). Then a big green **3**_____
(dinosaur, dragon) appeared. It was a **4**_____ (fierce,
friendly) dragon. The dragon said he did not eat **5**_____
(animals, humans). He said that he ate anything made of
6_____ (metal, wood). He said that metal made his tail
and **7**_____ (claws, wings) very strong. The dragon asked
Jasmine if she wanted to fly in the sky on his back. Jasmine
put her arms around his **8**_____ (tail, neck). The dragon's
scales were very **9**_____ (prickly, smooth). The dragon told
Jasmine not to get too near his **10**_____ (teeth, mouth). The
dragon flapped his wings and off they flew.

Sentences

Write each sentence again, and punctuate it correctly.

11 one day jasmine saw smoke coming out of a cave

_____

12 the dragon said i wont eat you

_____

Words

Write these words as contractions, for example: can not = can't.

13 do not _____   **14** it is _____   **15** I am _____

Mark your answers. How well did you do?

I scored ____ out of 15.

Road safety

Never play near a busy road. If you need to cross a road, learn how to do so safely.

Fire

Fire can help us but it can also be dangerous. Don't play with fire. It can soon get out of control and easily hurt you. Never play with matches or set fire to rubbish.

Electricity

Electricity can help us but can also be dangerous. The trouble is we cannot see electricity. Never push things into electrical sockets.

Water

We need water to live. We drink it and wash in it. It is fun to play in – but beware! It can harm you. Water in ponds and lakes can be very deep. In rivers and the sea, the water can move very fast. Sometimes you cannot see what is below the surface of the water. Some people dump rubbish and broken glass in it. Sometimes chemical waste is dumped in water. Sometimes the wildlife in water can be dangerous, too.

Checking understanding

Choose the best word to fill in each gap.

1 Never play near a _____ (busy, bushy) road.
2 Fire can _____ (help, hurt) us but it can also be dangerous.
3 Never play with _____ (patches, matches) or set fire to rubbish.
4 We cannot _____ (sea, see) electricity.
5 Never push things into electrical _____ (pockets, sockets).
6 We need water to _____ (dive, live).
7 We _____ (drink, sink) water and wash in it.
8 Water in ponds and _____ (cakes, lakes) can be very deep.
9 In rivers and the sea, the water can move _____ (fast, past).
10 Sometimes you cannot see what is below the _____ (bottom, surface) of the water.

Sentences

Complete each sentence with a sensible preposition.

11 It is dangerous to play _____ a busy road.
12 Never push things _____ electrical sockets.
13 Sometimes you cannot see what is _____ the surface of the water.

Words

Find a word on the poster that ends with:

14 'ous' _____   15 'ace' _____

Mark your answers. How well did you do?

I scored ____ out of 15.

Soon their spaceship was approaching Planet Octavia. In the distance were huge purple mountains, their tops covered with mist. 'Prepare for landing,' Captain Marriot ordered. He spotted a flat shelf of rock and landed the spacecraft safely.

Alex checked the atmosphere outside and discovered there was no air on the planet. She and Captain Marriot put on their spacesuits so they could breathe. They cautiously opened the door and stepped out onto the ground. The rocky ground crunched under their space boots. Nearby there were some strange tracks. 'It looks like some huge animal,' Alex said. 'Shall we follow them?'

'Yes, but be careful,' Captain Marriot warned. He held his laser gun firmly in his hand.

The tracks led them to a rocky valley. What they saw made them gasp with amazement. There, in the distance, was another spacecraft – but it was covered in a thick silver rope, like a giant spider's web. They followed the tracks towards a huge cave in a cliff. It was getting dark. Suddenly Captain Marriot shouted, 'Get down!' and pointed towards the cave. They quickly dived behind a rock.

Coming out of the cave was a huge space spider. Its body and legs were covered with thick, black hair. As it got closer and closer, its eyes turned a strange orange colour. The huge spider loomed over them and opened its massive jaws …

Checking understanding

Answer these questions.

1. What was the name of the planet? _____
2. Which two people were in the spaceship? _____
3. Where did they land on Planet Octavia? _____
4. What did Alex discover when she checked the outside atmosphere? _____
5. What did Captain Marriot and Alex see nearby? _____
6. What did Captain Marriot hold in his hand? _____
7. What made them gasp when they entered the rocky valley? _____
8. Where did the tracks lead? _____
9. What did the spider look like? _____
10. What happened to the spider's eyes as it got closer? _____

Sentences

Complete each sentence with a sensible adverb.

11. Captain Marriot landed the spacecraft _____.
12. They _____ opened the door.
13. Captain Marriot held his laser gun _____ in his hand.

Words

Find a word ending in:

14. 'ment' _____   15. 'ive' _____

Mark your answers. How well did you do?

I scored ____ out of 15.

Advertisements try to persuade us to buy things. Here are some of the ways they try to do it.

Key words that stand out

Name of product in capitals

Catchy jingle or rhyme

Attractive picture

Use of some well-chosen words

Appeals to everyone

Checking understanding

Answer these questions.

1. What do advertisements try to persuade us to do? _____
2. What product is this advertisement trying to sell? _____
3. Is the name of the product in capital letters? _____
4. What catchy jingle is the girl at the bottom saying? _____
5. How many times does the word 'new' appear? _____
6. What sentence tells you that Chock Stick is not just for children? _____
7. What does the advertisement say Chock Stick contains? _____
8. Where does it say it melts? _____
9. What does it say is terrific? _____
10. In one two-word phrase, both words begin with 'm'. Which phrase is it? _____

Sentences

11. How many exclamation marks are used in the advertisement? _____

Words

Find a word that ends with:

12. 'tion' _____
13. 'ive' _____
14. 'al' _____
15. 'ic' _____

Mark your answers. How well did you do?

I scored _____ out of 15.

33

Alfred the robot is a helpful machine.
He sweeps the house and keeps it clean.
He vacuums the carpet on the stairs
He polishes the table and the chairs.
He tidies my bedroom and picks up my clothes.
He gets me a tissue to blow my nose.

But one day something awful went wrong.
Crash! Bang! Thump! Bong!

Alfred started to make a terrible noise.
He went to my bedroom and broke all my toys.
He went to the kitchen and broke all the mugs.
He went to the front room and ate all the rugs.

Alfred the helpful – please be a good machine.
You are much nicer when you keep the house clean!

Checking understanding

Write T (true) or F (false) after each sentence.

1. Alfred is a robot. _____
2. Alfred sweeps the garden. _____
3. He vacuums the carpet on the stairs. _____
4. He polishes shoes. _____
5. He washes clothes. _____
6. When Alfred went wrong, he made a terrible noise. _____
7. He went to the bedroom and broke all the toys. _____
8. He went to the bathroom and broke all the mugs. _____
9. He went to the kitchen and ate all the rugs. _____
10. Alfred is nicer when he keeps the house clean. _____

Sentences

Complete each sentence with a sensible verb.

11. Alfred _____ the carpet on the stairs.
12. Alfred _____ my bedroom.
13. Alfred _____ the table and the chairs.

Words

Which word rhymes with:

14. machine _____

15. noise _____

Mark your answers. How well did you do?

I scored ____ out of 15.

It was a sunny afternoon in the summer holidays. Mia and Jack were bored. Their friends had all gone away on holiday. They had nothing to do. Suddenly Jack said, 'Let's ask Mum if we can take Max to the park.' (The park was nearby, just at the end of their road.)

'That's a great idea!' Mia replied. Mum said it was all right but told the children to be home by four o'clock. Max the dog was lying asleep in the sun, by the window. As soon as he heard Mia and Jack getting his lead, his eyes sprang open and he jumped to his feet, wagging his tail. Jack put Max on the lead and off they went.

They soon reached the park. First they went to the pond and watched some children feeding bread to the ducks. Then they went to the playground, where there were swings, a slide and a roundabout. Jack tied Max's lead to a bench and then he and Mia played on the swings. Time seemed to speed by. When Mia looked at her watch it was nearly four o'clock. 'Come on Jack! It's time to go. Let's get Max and head for home,' Mia said.

But when Mia and Jack went to untie Max's lead from the bench they had a nasty shock. The lead was there but the dog had disappeared!

'Oh no!' Jack cried. 'Max has escaped!'

'We'd better look for him!' Mia said. So they began searching for the missing dog. They looked behind bushes. They looked near the pond. They shouted at the top of their voices – but Max was nowhere to be seen. Mia looked at her watch again. It was already after four o'clock. Mia and Jack didn't know what to do.

'Shall we carry on looking for Max?' Jack asked.

'Shall I go and get Mum?' Mia asked.

'Shall we go to the police station and report Max missing?' Jack said. If you were Mia or Jack, what would you do?

Checking understanding

Answer these questions.

1. Was it the summer or winter? _____
2. Was the park a long way from Mia and Jack's house? _____
3. Where was Max lying asleep? _____
4. What did Max do when he realised Mia and Jack were going out? _____
5. What did the children do first at the park? _____
6. What did Jack do to Max? _____
7. Who had a watch – Mia or Jack? _____
8. How do you think the children felt when they realised Max was missing? _____
9. Where did Mia and Jack look first? _____
10. Did they try calling out to Max? _____

Sentences

Write each sentence again, and punctuate it correctly.

11. mia and jack had nothing to do so they took max to the park

_____

12. mum said you must be home by four o clock

_____

Words

Do these word sums and make some compound words.

13. after + noon = _____   14. play + ground = _____

15. near + by = _____

Mark your answers. How well did you do?

I scored ____ out of 15.

Here is the original version:

Solomon Grundy
Was born on Monday.
Was christened on Tuesday.
Got married on Wednesday.
Was ill on Thursday.
Got worse on Friday.
Died on Saturday.
Was buried on Sunday.
And that was the end of Solomon Grundy.

Here is a modern version:

Solomon Grundy
Got measles on Monday.
Fell in a puddle on Tuesday.
Tore his trousers on Wednesday.
Got stuck in a lift on Thursday.
Had stomach ache on Friday.
Crashed his car on Saturday.
Was chased by a gorilla on Sunday.
And that was the end of Solomon Grundy.

Checking understanding

Answer these questions from the original version.

1. On which day was Solomon Grundy born? _____
2. On which day did he get married? _____
3. What happened on Thursday? _____
4. Why was Saturday a sad day? _____
5. What happened on Sunday? _____

Now answer these questions from the modern version.

6. What did Solomon get on Monday? _____
7. Why wasn't Tuesday a good day for him? _____
8. What happened on Thursday? _____
9. Why wasn't Friday any better? _____
10. What happened on Sunday? _____

Sentences

Complete each sentence from the modern version with a sensible verb.

11. What did Solomon do on Tuesday? He _____ in a puddle.
12. What did he do on Wednesday? He _____ his trousers.
13. What did he do on Saturday? He _____ his car.

Words

14. In the original version, the 'ch' in 'christened' sounds like 'k'. In the modern version, two words contain 'ch' which also sound like 'k'. What are they? _____ _____
15. What small three-letter word is hiding in 'gorilla'? _____

Mark your answers. How well did you do?

I scored ____ out of 15.

Shajan has a new penfriend. Here is the first letter he received.

24 Castle Street
Dover
Kent
CT16 2YZ

13th July

Dear Shajan

I live at the seaside. My house is near the seafront. There is a harbour where lots of boats come and go. I love to watch the lorries and cars coming off the ferries from France.

I like going to the beach and swimming in the sea, especially in the summer when it is hot. In Dover we get a lot of visitors from all over the world.

Behind Dover there is a large hill. At the top of the hill there is an old castle. You can visit it and see the dungeons where prisoners were kept. From the top of the castle you can see for miles.

Near Dover there are farms that grow fruit like apples and cherries. There are lots more interesting things in my town, but I will tell you about them another time. Do write to me and tell me something about the place where you live.

Love
James

Checking understanding

Choose the best word to fill in each gap.

1. The letter is from _____ (Shajan, James).
2. James lives in _____ (Dover, France).
3. James's house is near the _____ (castle, seafront).
4. James watches lorries coming off the _____ (beach, ferries).
5. Dover gets lots of _____ (visitors, seagulls).
6. There is a large _____ (harbour, hill) behind Dover.
7. A _____ (church, castle) stands on top of the hill.
8. In the castle there are some _____ (prisoners, dungeons).
9. From the _____ (side, top) of the castle you can see for miles.
10. James wrote the letter in _____ (June, July).

Sentences

Write each sentence again, and punctuate it correctly.

11. james lives in castle street dover

    _____

12. james likes to see the lorries from france

    _____

Words

Spell these plurals correctly:

13. one lorry but two _____
14. one ferry but two _____
15. one cherry but two _____

Mark your answers. How well did you do?

I scored _____ out of 15.

41

Early life

Diana Spencer was born in 1961. She lived in a big country house. Her family was very rich and knew Queen Elizabeth and other members of the British royal family. Diana always loved children. When she left school, she got a job in a kindergarten. She helped to look after young children.

Prince Charles

One day Diana met Prince Charles, the Queen's eldest son. In 1981 the prince asked Diana to marry him. The wedding took place in July of that year in London. Millions of people watched the wedding on television. Some people said Diana was like a princess from a fairytale. As Charles was called the Prince of Wales, Diana became the Princess of Wales.

Having a family

In 1982 Diana had a baby son. She called him William. Two years later, in 1984, she had a second son called Harry. One day her eldest son, William, will become king.

Helping people

Diana loved meeting and being with people. She was always gentle, friendly and kind to everyone. Wherever she went, crowds of people gathered to see her. People said that Diana was just like an ordinary person. Diana was very good at raising money for people in need. She helped all sorts of people – the old, the blind and the sick. She loved helping children.

Her death

In Paris, on 31 August 1997, the car Diana was travelling in crashed. Diana was killed in the accident. She was only 36 years old. When Diana died, even people who had never met her were sad. The whole world was shocked at her death. Thousands of people put flowers outside her home. She was such a popular and well-loved person that more than a million people watched her funeral on the television. Diana is buried on a small island at her home in England where she lived as a child.

Checking understanding

Write T (true) or F (false) after each sentence.

1. Diana Spencer was born in 1961. _____
2. When Diana left school she went to work in an office. _____
3. Diana married Prince Charles in 1981. _____
4. Diana became known as the Princess of Scotland. _____
5. In 1982 Diana had a son called Harry. _____
6. One day Diana's elder son, William, will become king. _____
7. Diana was very shy, and did not like meeting people. _____
8. Diana was very good at raising money for people in need. _____
9. Diana was killed in a road accident in 1998. _____
10. She was only 36 years old when she died. _____

Sentences

Complete each sentence with a proper noun, for example, a person's name.

11. In 1981 _____ asked Diana to marry him.
12. Prince Charles is the eldest son of _____.
13. Princess Diana had two sons called _____ and _____.

Words

In some words 'c' sounds like 's' and 'g' sounds like 'j'. Fill in the missing 'c' or 'g' in these words:

14. __entle
15. prin__ess

Mark your answers. How well did you do?

I scored ____ out of 15.

Answers

Test 1
1 Helen
2 Menelaus
3 to rescue Helen
4 yes
5 a huge wooden horse
6 inside the wooden horse
7 through the gates and into the city
8 home
9 that night
10 because the Trojans were asleep
11 Long ago there was a beautiful Greek princess called Helen.
12 Menelaus sailed to Troy to rescue Helen.
13 fought
14 could
15 door

Test 2
1 T
2 F
3 T
4 F
5 T
6 F
7 T
8 F
9 T
10 T
11 new
12 drowsy
13 shady
14 drummed
15 shiver

Test 3
1 burrows
2 dusk
3 plants
4 setts
5 night
6 mice
7 dens
8 animals
9 drey
10 nuts
11 live
12 look
13 eat
14 underground
15 sometimes

Test 4
1 eight
2 yes
3 rain
4 bloom
5 the sun
6 rivers
7 The sea goes on forever
8 Verse 5
9 Verse 7
10 we grow older day by day
11 bloom, fade
12 drizzles, falls
13 moon
14 river
15 rain

Test 5

1. T
2. F
3. F
4. T
5. T
6. F
7. T
8. T
9. F
10. T
11. The yellow butterfly asked the yellow rose, 'May we stop here?'
12. 'You may,' replied the rose. 'You are the same colour as I am.'
13. unkind
14. disappear
15. unwell

Test 6

1. a mouse, a frog and a little red hen
2. Little Red Hen
3. the mouse and the frog
4. rye
5. a bowl and a spoon
6. make a roaring fire
7. 'Not I,' said the sleepy frog with a yawn. 'Nor I,' said the mouse again.
8. 'I will!' cried the frog. 'And I!' squeaked the mouse.
9. no
10. She flew away with it.
11. lazy
12. roaring
13. sleepy
14. croak
15. roar

Test 7

1. hot
2. well
3. thin
4. stone
5. water
6. rope
7. inside
8. poured
9. Bob
10. boot
11. Bob was very, very hot.
12. As Bob got closer, he saw a dog near the well.
13. 'Water!' cried Bob excitedly.
14. desperate
15. picture

Test 8

1. Mark
2. Ivan
3. Kevin
4. Alice
5. Florence
6. Jade
7. Carol
8. Ben
9. Edward
10. Georgia
11. O is for Olivia who breaks all her toys.
12. P is for Petra who plays with the boys.
13. cheating drinking eating

14 licking pulling washing
15 sharing shouting shutting

Test 9

1   T
2   T
3   F
4   F
5   T
6   T
7   T
8   F
9   T
10 T
11 grows
12 bakes
13 buy
14 cough
15 leaf

Test 10

1   by lamps in the ceiling
2   a gold key
3   forty centimetres high
4   to look through the door
5   the loveliest garden she had ever seen
6   a telescope
7   there was a bottle on the table
8   all of Alice's favourite foods
9   twenty centimetres high
10 Lewis Carroll
11 on
12 behind
13 through
14 kneel
15 writing

Test 11

1   Siberia
2   flat, country
3   powerful
4   strike, roots
5   scatter
6   destroy, tightly
7   wake, worthless
8   corn, field
9   blow, hearth
10 same
11 traditional
12 flat
13 powerful
14 wonderful
15 careful

Test 12

1   smoke
2   cave
3   dragon
4   friendly
5   humans
6   metal
7   wings
8   neck
9   prickly
10 mouth
11 One day Jasmine saw smoke coming out of a cave.
12 The dragon said, 'I won't eat you.'
13 don't
14 it's
15 I'm

Test 13

1 busy
2 help
3 matches
4 see
5 sockets
6 live
7 drink
8 lakes
9 fast
10 surface
11 near
12 into
13 under
14 dangerous
15 surface

Test 14

1 Octavia
2 Captain Marriot and Alex
3 on a flat shelf of rock
4 There was no air on the planet.
5 some strange tracks
6 his laser gun
7 another spacecraft covered in a thick silver rope
8 towards a huge cave in a cliff
9 It was huge. Its body and legs were covered with thick, black hair.
10 They turned a strange green colour.
11 safely
12 cautiously
13 firmly
14 amazement
15 massive

Test 15

1 to buy things
2 Chock Stick – the ice cream on a stick
3 yes
4 I scream, you scream. We all scream for ice cream!
5 two
6 Chock Stick – it's a treat for all the family
7 nuts, chocolate and ice cream
8 in your mouth
9 its new taste
10 magical moments
11 seven on actual poster (also one in girl's speech bubble at bottom of page)
12 sensation
13 attractive
14 magical
15 terrific

Test 16

1 T
2 F
3 T
4 F
5 F
6 T
7 T
8 F
9 F
10 T
11 vacuums
12 tidies
13 polishes
14 clean
15 toys

Test 17

1 summer
2 no
3 in the sun, by the window
4 his eyes sprang open and he jumped to his feet, wagging his tail
5 went to the pond and watched some children feeding bread to the ducks
6 tied Max's lead to a bench
7 Mia
8 open – accept any suitable and appropriate answer
9 behind bushes
10 yes
11 Mia and Jack had nothing to do so they took Max to the park.
12 Mum said, 'You must be home by four o'clock.'
13 afternoon
14 playground
15 nearby

Test 18

1 Monday
2 Wednesday
3 He was ill.
4 Solomon Grundy died.
5 He was buried.
6 measles
7 He fell in a puddle.
8 He got stuck in a lift.
9 He had a stomach ache.
10 He was chased by a gorilla.
11 fell
12 tore
13 crashed
14 stomach ache
15 ill

Test 19

1 James
2 Dover
3 seafront
4 ferries
5 visitors
6 hill
7 castle
8 dungeons
9 top
10 July
11 James lives in Castle Street, Dover.
12 James likes to see the lorries from France.
13 lorries
14 ferries
15 cherries

Test 20

1 T
2 F
3 T
4 F
5 F
6 T
7 F
8 T
9 F
10 T
11 Prince Charles
12 Queen Elizabeth
13 William and Harry
14 gentle
15 princess